THE
UMZINDUSI
LETTER

By

TIM TOPPS

Does this solve the Lord Erroll mystery?

I can still hardly believe it myself.

Alan Broad

Matador
9 Priory Business Park,
Wistow Road, Kibworth Beauchamp,
Leicestershire. LE8 0RX
Tel: 0116 279 2299
Email: books@troubador.co.uk
Web: www.troubador.co.uk/matador
Twitter: @matadorbooks

ISBN 9781788033619

British Library Cataloguing in Publication Data.
A catalogue record for this book is available from the British Library.

Printed and bound in the UK by TJ International, Padstow, Cornwall

Matador is an imprint of Troubador Publishing Ltd

Out of the blue at the end of March 1941, my grandfather (with whom I spent my school holidays throughout the Second World War) received a brief letter from Winston Churchill, whom he had never met nor had dealings with.

Though Prime Minister, the great man had written on Foreign Office notepaper, but we thought little of that at the time. It only became a lot more significant some months ago (and I am writing in December 2016), when I happened to rediscover it. The letter carries a full reference number, but I'm told that the file has been destroyed. I think I know why.

"My Umzindusi Grandfather" the Ninth Lancer

Grandad had been through the Boer War in the Ninth Lancers and when we went to church on Sundays he would brush down my suit, puffing as if I was a horse. He was that strange Victorian hybrid: a deeply religious (Cornish Methodist) professional cavalryman. When they retired to Tadworth in the outer London suburbs (and right on the Nazi bombers flight-path as it transpired) he named their house after a South African river that flowed past their Army base: 'Umzindusi' was, apparently, 'The Saviour', because it never dried up.

Grandad never dried up either, but I loved his constant reminiscences, especially about their only son, my father, growing up as a 'son of the regiment' out there in the early 1900s. Dad was now again in Africa, as we had gone to Kenya in 1934 and after coming back for the 1937 Coronation, my parents had returned to their UK Trade Commissioner service in Nairobi (travelling, coincidentally, with the Baden-Powells) while I was left at boarding-school, not to see them again for seven years. It so happened that both Dad and my Lancer Grandad had been keenly involved with the Boy Scout Movement ever since its early days, running a whatever-they're-called, first in South London and latterly in Surrey; and Dad had formed a Rover group

1

in Nairobi soon after we arrived, so successful that he was appointed Rover Commissioner for all British East Africa, and was already well-known to Baden-Powell. His Rovers were now also working in conjunction with Kenya Special Police on various missions in the precarious days of the late 1930s.

Seventy-five years ago last January (as I write) Lord Baden-Powell finally died at his much-loved home, not far from Nairobi; two weeks later, the high security risk and Fascist-inclined Lord Erroll was shot dead in his car on the Nairobi-Ngong road. It was January 1941.

No writer until now, so far as I know, has made any connection between these two sad events. The link, I am now pretty sure, or a big part of that link, must be my father. There are strong family hints which only I could ever have known, and others I've recently discovered, about both Dad and Baden-Powell, that culminate in the small cache which includes the Umzindusi letter, however succinct.

At my age of 89 I am probably the only witness remaining with new evidence to offer, and even with personal memories of some of the people involved. The strongest of these is of old BP himself...

* * *

The Umzindusi River at Pietermaritzburg

II

When I was chatting with Baden-Powell in Nairobi in 1935, we were both in short trousers: he as part of the Chief Scout uniform, I at age eight. He had been impressed by the Rover squad that had met him at the station, under my Dad, and I remember he was telling me, to my astonishment, that his own father had been born before Napoleon came to power. That struck me (or would have in the language of today) as 'very cool' indeed...

Tell it not, but I wasn't in the least attracted to Scouting myself; too much of it going on around me. All the time – even Mum was constantly making sandwiches and churning out jacket potatoes... there were knots everywhere!

And I remember that even then I saw BP more as a wily old soldier. I knew all about Mafeking, its siege and relief (it was little over 30 years ago and, to me then, 'just down the coast'), and his book about spying was on Dad's shelf in the study. Above all, he'd had the glamorous panache to put his own head on an official postage stamp, and get away with it! Indeed a hero.

* * *

This was somewhere in the back of my ageing mind, I suppose, when three years ago, writing my mainly fictional book about the rise and fall of my student insurance business, I gave myself a great shock in Chapter 12. It's easiest just to reprint those pages in order to bring you into the Erroll story. At this point, completely fictional, I am about to be blackmailed by an old Professor ...

Baden Powell inspecting Dad's Rover Scouts (Dad on near right)

B-P wrote in his diary, 18th Nov 1935

"Arrived Nairobi 9.20am. Met at station by Hon. E.G. Morris (President for Kenya) ... Also a Posse of Welcome of a newly-formed Rover crew of European ex-Scouts, 15 fine fellows. A very smart lot, most of them being members of the Defence Force."

From 'Too Long in the Business' by Tim Topps (Matador 2014)

My first writing about the Erroll affair, supposedly fictional, but, as I gradually realised, alarmingly significant!

* * *

The Signor Professore was ageing before my eyes. No longer was Dorian in the attic: he had come downstairs with sombre tread, I thought to myself as I sat in the usual chair. He watched me with a gloomy countenance and a rather wheezing breath, while still stroking the cat. The animal had aged, too, and it blinked more slowly.

Dr Oxdon was alert, however, to what I had to say. Poised, I sensed. But I had come here to see if I could eliminate him from our suspect list. After all, I reasoned, it was he who had got us all the student data in the first place, so why use us when he already had that mysterious access? I took a deep breath: but –

"Have a cape gooseberry."

He was pointing to some marble-sized orange fruits in a bowl on the beautiful oak joint-stool beside me, splendid with its fluted legs.

"Good heavens," I exclaimed, "I haven't seen those since – "

"Yes, since in your garden in Nairobi? You don't often find them here, I'm told. A friend flew in. They have that nickname, don't they, in Africa. Scientifically the name sounds like a nasty Schubertian disease: Physalis."

"Perhaps," I said, taking one, "one should eat it with a pinch of mercury?"

That, he liked. Not for the first time I felt that he had become a lonely old man, aching for lightweight, even flippant conversation; for many years no tutorials with young students; little attendance any more at Top Tables even when he felt physically able; drink invitations from the SCR, so few now; most contemporaries gone, and all these new people with their loud voices so that you couldn't hear what that nice old fellow next to you was saying. And you see, as soon as we started to chat inconsequentially, he was blossoming. I remembered how he had clearly relished the Scrutton 'Garden of Cucumbers'; and I wondered whether he would appreciate Olivia's Italian version of Pooh – I thought it was very likely, must send it to him… But now I had to be severe and talk business. It shouldn't be difficult…

"The CIA have been in contact with me," I began, in a suitably sensational tone, just to shake him.

"Oh dear" he responded blandly and in complete calm. "Has all this student stuff of yours been dragged into politics? That's the last thing you want."

As before with this whimsical old man, I found it difficult to get my message through.

I said: "You've been asking for our data on students' insurances for several years, and I've been happy to oblige because your initial introduction admittedly let us establish our – now excellent – relationships with the student unions; but now it will have to stop."

7

There – I'd said it. "Stop absolutely," I ended.

Oxdon nodded, but I was sure that he wasn't in any way agreeing with me, he was just waiting for me to take a breath. It was that indulgent sort of 'finish-your-essay' nod. The cat stretched up rheumatically and rubbed against his chin. He smiled at me in a friendly and reassuring way. I didn't much like it.

"Tell me, Tim," he asked as he helped himself from the porcelain bowl, "We do a lot of research and I need you just to confirm a few – er – facts. Yes," he added thoughtfully, "Facts. Is it correct that your parents have just come home and retired?"

Well, yes they had, two years ago, down in Sussex. But what was this?

"And he was in the Overseas Civil Service? Stationed in Kenya in the Forties, down among the gooseberries?"

"Yes," I agreed again, puzzled. "We went out in 1934 and though I came home to school with them at Coronation time in thirty-seven, they went back and were there through most of the war. Why?"

Oxdon obviously knew all this already and was simply setting the scenery for something I couldn't possibly guess. He had leant asthmatically back in his chair, and waited for a short while, eyeing me over the top of those glasses, even now slightly askew.

Then it came: "What was your father's connection with Baden Powell?"

The incongruous question threw me into a sort of Wimp's Wonderland. What on earth had been cooked up, seemingly to cast doubts in some unspoken way upon my Dad's friendship with the founder of the Boy Scouts?

My reply in bewilderment: "Dad, and *his* father too, had been very early supporters of Scouting, following the family's return from South Africa – Potchefstroom I think – with the Ninth Lancers soon after the Boer War. They started a Troop in South London, at Wimbledon – "

"Southfields, actually." He nodded me on.

"Dad was only in his early teens, but enthusiastic from the start – he was that sort of chap. In fact, he even acted as a schoolboy air-raid warden in 1914-18, and also won a Scout medal for stopping a – "

"Runaway horse and cart, yes. We have that. He was awarded what they call 'The Scouts VC', wasn't he?"

"For goodness sake," I was getting rankled by all this, "what is there you don't know? And whyever is this relevant?"

Oxdon nodded again, presumably to appear understanding. But he waved me on.

"Well then, the bits I personally remember. Dad's daytime job was sales promotion for the UK Government, he used to call on masses of local firms, putting British exporters in touch. He sometimes took me with him," and I remembered with a chuckle, "Once we were at a vast pyrethrum farm and I floored him by asking, if it was such a powerful insecticide, however did it spread its pollen? But after-hours, he was soon appointed Chief Rover Scout for all of East Africa: that is," quoting from the postage stamps I knew so well: "Kenya, Uganda and Tanganyika – oh, and Zanzibar."

9

Zanzibar had always seemed to me as a kid out there, a highly exotic add-on to Dad's territory. It was a slight disappointment when I finally got there on the way home, just cloves and white buildings and a lot of palm trees, except for that exciting wrecked German cruiser at the entrance to the harbour – or was that Dar-es-Salaam?

"And though all this Scouting activity was a sideline," I continued, "In all his spare time after his Governmental Trade Promotion work, he did it very well, really in depth, starting new troops for young Indians and Africans too, which BP greatly approved of, I've got his letters saying so. Just before the war he started a secret night-time Special Police team using his Rovers and their friends – "

"Forgive me, dear boy, but what about 'BP' himself? How close was your father to him? He had retired to live in the Kenya uplands at the end of his life, and we know that your father was listed as being one of the pall-bearers when he died; all that, we have. But why?"

"Why do you want to know?"

"We have a theory and a suspicion. All this will emerge as we continue. Now: how did BP get close to Dad?"

"After leaving me at school in 1937, they went back on, I think, the 'Llangibby Castle', one of the work-horses of the Union Castle Line which sailed to Africa 'every Friday at four o'clock'".

"Thursday."

"And Mum and Dad, being in the middle stratum of Governmental big-wigs, and as it was a small ship, found themselves at the same table as the BPs. Naturally, the

10

Scouting connection came up; and they got quite close, sharing all the official visits the BPs had to make, showing-the-flag at Scouting stops along the way, acting as his aide-de-camp, I suppose you'd say."

"And when they all got to Kenya?"

"BP stayed pretty close to Dad. He didn't meet many people after that because he was ageing, and happily tucked away on his upcountry estate; but he and Dad received and sent lots of paperwork and information from time to time; and BP kept a keen eye on the Rover Scout development as it made such a good contribution to the war effort out there. The Rovers were really close to the Police; and Dad told me many Kenyans were very negative just then about our prospects against the Italians – who were massing on the northern border."

"Oh, very negative. We'll come on to that. Now, about Baden-Powell: did you know that in his earlier days, Army days during the Boer War, he had ordered executions?"

"I can't say I knew that, but I'm sure in wartime – "

"… and made a point of going to watch them?"

"A senior officer has to, Doctor, you must know that. And in those days of guerrilla warfare –"

"In other words, BP was no saint when the opportunity arose – "

I was incensed by this. Was Oxdon beginning to dement? I spluttered so vehemently that the cat jumped off him: "Doctor, your choice of words is disgraceful. How can you say 'the opportunity… Necessity, perhaps?" Where was this going?

11

He shrugged. "Ach, that is just semantics. I accept your criticism, largely because you are understandably in support of your father, and of course you only knew BP as a kindly old famous gentlemanly Peer of the Realm, not so?"

The accumulation of adjectives was an irritation, but I had to ignore it.

"Exactly what he was," I said, "Every word. My father was very proud to have known him, and greatly regretted he couldn't be a pall-bearer as intended, as he was away in the RAF."

"Ah!"

As usual, this old man was ahead of me. He looked at me thoughtfully, then picked up a sheet of paper on which I could see scribblings, not in green ink thankfully but in a sort of Quink purple which was bad enough. Green would have been a possible hint of incipient madness; purple couldn't be far off. Some newspaper cuttings were pinned to it, even more alarming...

"Erroll." He looked at me over those glasses again. "What does that name mean to you?"

'Flynn', was my immediate response, as if we were playing psychological games... Robin Hood... sexy young girls naked in showers... phoney swordfights... bloody Australian... 'Too Much Too Soon', and you can say that again.

I said with a laugh: "Were there Boy Scouts in Sherwood Forest then?"

He didn't smile: not even a bit. I realised that something tricky was coming up. He apologetically cleared his throat, and out it came.

"No," he said. "*Lord* Erroll. Working in Nairobi, ostensibly for the Government. Appointed, astonishingly, given his background, to be Kenya's Defence Secretary or some such official post just when Italy threatened to invade. Fascist. Very active at the Muthaiga Club your parents belonged to. Extremely popular with the ladies, especially the married ones with husbands safely away at the war."

I thought his neat phrase 'safely away at the war' was a good paradox, for use in some other context; but not this one.

"Shot dead," Oxdon went on. "In his car. Late night of 24th January, 1941." A pause as he looked across at me. "A few days after BP's funeral. Shot close-up behind the left ear, and of course it was a right-hand drive. Old fourteen-eighteen gun, the suspected weapon, but that means nothing; but black powder, which was strange... He was found by natives not far from his home on the Ngong road, it was presumed having had an assignation on the plains. Gun never found."

I did now recall the basic facts behind this murder, I must have read about it vaguely at school, I suppose, but at that time, aged fourteen, we were more concerned with the Blitz directly above us, and – only secondly – newspaper front pages with their sketch-maps along the North Africa coast, with names like Sidi Barrani and Tobruk (which fell that very week, I now see). So, with an effort, what could I remember?

A local high-living member of the Happy Valley crowd, Delves-Broughton, a baronet cuckolded by Erroll, had been charged but acquitted. It hadn't been Broughton's gun, forensic discovered at the trial. Nobody else had been nailed for this shooting, and frankly, few liked Erroll in any case, widely believed a Fascist. And it was wartime, which by common consent, not least among the local judiciary, forgave a lot. It had never really registered in my long-term memory, too remote, but these snippets came back to me.

"So," Oxdon pulled me back to the present, "what do you know about Erroll, from your parents?"

It wasn't difficult really, once prompted, and given that my Kenya memories were so pleasant, to wade back through years of childhood to those happy days in Thirties Nairobi, when at the age of eight my friend Brian and I would cycle completely safely and carefree down into the centre of town, update our stamp collections at the shop of the East African Standard newspaper, call on Dad at Memorial Hall across the road, pop into the powerful concrete Art Deco covered market to pick up something to chew, and then ride past Brian's father's pharmacy to the picture-house, there to watch in complete absorption the latest Astaire and Rogers that our parents had been raving about at breakfast.

But whatever was all this about Erroll? I had to say: "Dad never even mentioned him, he might have been a Top Brass, but we weren't in that circle at all. No connection whatever to the boring Happy Valley crowd, whom, if anything, one despised while envying their money.

"Dad was only a Muthaiga member ex-officio, he was

14

just a middle-range Home UK Civil Servant out there on a thousand a year. They couldn't afford Muthaiga unless somebody invited them, could they?"

"They sent you to the private Muthaiga School nearby."

And I scored this time. "Indeed, at a considerable sacrifice to help my education, and that's why they couldn't afford to go to the Club. And then when I was back home in England, with them paying for my schooling still, Dad was – "

"Away at the war, yes. Adjutant at RAF Khartoum. Very hot and sweaty." He looked up from the purple notes. "And back in Nairobi, where was your mother putting in her war work?"

I remembered a few chatty bits of scandal she had enjoyed passing on to me when we finally met up after the war, out in Canada, and suddenly, to my astonishment, I could see where this was going.

* * *

With excellent shorthand and general office skills remembered from her secretarial work in the Twenties, Mum's wartime job in Kenya had been in the typing-pool, first at a Government House annexe, close to the Arboretum and just down the road from our house on Chiromo Road, and later up near the Muthaiga district. The office, I now half-remembered, was run – largely in his absence – by the glamorous Lord Erroll; and on the rare occasions that he showed up in office hours, he was inclined to – as Mum put it – "come and sit on our desks and chat, ooh he was lovely." Nothing more. But now, Oxdon had swiftly made it important.

Dad was away.

Oxdon said casually: "So Erroll was quite a lady killer – quite a catch – among the forlorn abandoned wives of the Muthaiga sorority?"

"Well, I don't suppose he was the only predator in those days in Happy Valley, in a wartime society that had already been decadent for half a century. But my family were among the run-of-the-mill governmental crowd, quite removed from the settlers in Happy – "

"Of course, but people like Erroll hunted away from home, as well." He sat up in his armchair and reached out to switch on a standard lamp – I hadn't even noticed that daylight had been fading.

"He was thirty-nine when he died. Your Mum – ?"

I had to think. "Forty-one."

"Tim, you need to know this," he began gently, though surely it was a contrived gentleness? "The Erroll murder, after Delves-Broughton was cleared, has never been solved. It's still wide open – "

Me, searching my memory: "Surely, Broughton killed himself?"

"Yes, at the Adelphi in Liverpool, but that was later on and nothing to do with Kenya or Erroll, we believe. We know he had other reasons."

For the first time I noticed the 'we'. Who was behind all this?

He turned on a beatific smile. It horrified me. I had learnt to accept the tentative half-smile which appeared on occasions, but that had been his genuine response to anything at all 'smile-worthy'. What I had here was an entirely artificial display, and I felt it was pulled by a puppet-master behind the scenes. I know a politician like that, and it's not nice. I began to realise that I was being set up, even though all these events were from another, distasteful world and nothing whatever –

"Hear me out," he said. "Forget the decadent Happy Valley crowd; we don't think Erroll's was a personal jealousy killing at all. None of them had the courage and anyway none of them were sexually jealous, there's any amount of evidence in their overall behaviour, don't you know?"

"So why is my mother – "

"Hear me. Erroll was a high security risk in 1941. He wasn't just leaning towards Fascism, in fact he had already joined Mosley's lot in 1934, which probably wasn't very widely known just yet among the general populace in Kenya. But now, bear in mind, the Italians, at war with us, were only just across the northern border, with their colonies on the Horn, and they had now moved into Abyssinia too, and were massing their troops. And here was Erroll the Fascist in charge of Defence, or part of it. Picture that."

I was picturing it, vividly. Despite myself I was finding his expert presentation fascinating. Oxdon could see this, and he called to the kitchen: "Could we have some cocoa or something, dear?" Turning to me: "Sugar?"

A voice came back: "On its way."

17

"You can see, Tim, they had a problem. With all his liaisons, Erroll was very likely to give important things away. He never had been able to keep a secret, especially between the sheets. And now, invasion was a big threat. He had to be stopped, and shut up."

"Why not just that – sack him and lock him up?"

"He would just talk all the more, and all his hoity-toity friends would kick up such a song and dance: lots of them were unreliable too. No, he had to be got rid of. He was odious anyway: I met him once. Do have a gooseberry."

I was trying to piece all this together. "Are you about to suggest that Baden Powell was behind this 'elimination'?" It was unbelievable.

"Well," he replied thoughtfully, "Remember BP's whole life had been on the top floor of the Establishment, and he was no stranger to the highest people in Intelligence, was he? And he had long been both a successful warrior and steeped in covert work – perhaps the only one in Kenya, and we were at war."

A sip of cocoa.

"As it happened, BP had met Erroll a couple of times early in 1940. In fact, sent him a polite neighbourly note on his new marriage, to which I gather he had no acknowledgment whatever, and that would have registered badly with the old man. But no doubt he would have been receiving feedback on the fellow from Security locally and from Intelligence higher up". He looked at me thoughtfully over his glasses. "I mean, Tim, who better? He would know what had to be done."

He stopped for a cough and a drop of cocoa went on to the cat, who licked at it lazily.

"Of course, the old man was on his last legs..." (look who's talking, I thought), "but we think he may have been asked to recommend someone he could trust to do the job." He looked at me yet again over those slanting glasses.

My Dad? Kill anyone? He even stepped over grasshoppers. He must mean one of Dad's Rovers. I wouldn't know about that, I told Oxdon.

"Someone he could really, really trust. This was an essential act of patriotism, with all our East African territory in mortal danger, let alone all the lives at risk. Kenya was almost undefended: most of the KAR were up in the desert."

"So was Dad."

"I'll come on to that." Ominous.

"We think that your father may have refused at first, but then agreed when the risks were explained to him; but he asked for the job to be postponed until BP died, to ensure that if the truth came out, any scandal would not in any way tarnish the Scout movement. Of course everybody knew that BP was fast fading. He died earlier that January and the shooting was on the 24th, remember?"

"Is there any evidence to support your silly story?" I was justified in being rude, the way this was going, and without any cigarettes.

He referred again to the purple ink. "Not a thing – "
"Well, then – "
"Except, you see, all the background circumstances.

Let us count them: One: the timing, as we've just discussed. No sooner is BP dead – "

"But Dad was away in the RAF – "

"Precisely, and therefore – two – he was subject to military orders, which would not have been the case before he went. And so: under orders, having a good alibi on the surface, while a fast little RAF plane could get him in from Khartoum to their private airport out on the plains outside Nairobi, and back again, very comfortably... There would have been a car waiting." He laid down the cocoa cup. "You should drink some more of this, it's very calming."

"You were about to list the background circumstances."

"Of course. Three: the means. I've just covered that, he could get there very easily, and very privately with RAF back-up. Four: The motive. Clearly, national interest. But you see, Tim, that if your father had been caught, he would be on his own – this is commonplace and both he and BP would have accepted that. Operatives are always 'on their own', aren't they? Read any novel. If things had gone wrong and Dad had been caught, perhaps by some late-night passer-by, he would simply have been arrested and presented to the Courts as a jealous husband, the perfect line to take by the authorities, no matter how much your Dad or Mum might have argued their innocence." Another break for a cough. "Five: the lack of anything else having emerged since – there haven't been any convincing deathbed confessions – "

"I thought – "

He shook his head. "Only a couple of silly Happy Valley freaks, like you always get, sozzled neurotic sensation-seekers looking for a headline, and they can all be dismissed; and not even in that crowd has anyone come forward to say anything really helpful. But more to the point, the official investigations petered out very quickly; reading transcripts of the trial, one would suspect the lawyers had been told to play the whole affair down. Nobody liked the man, only his title I suppose. All the obvious suspects had domestic alibis – "

"Supplied by their terrified wives?"

"Husbands, just as likely."

I tried common-sense. "You know you have nothing whatever against my father, let alone my mother. She did make occasional jokey references to Erroll, I remember now, when reminiscing about her wartime job, but Dad," I stupidly emphasised, "has never mentioned him at all, in all these years." But I knew at once that I had blown my case for the defence...

"Six," said Oxdon, and waited while it sank in.

Then he went on: "One has to ask: why not?" Short pause. "Isn't it the sort of event that any normal Kenya veteran from 1941 might occasionally reminisce about?"

"Oh, and number seven: why did your so-close-to-BP Dad not fly down for the funeral? As you said, he was listed, actually reported in the papers, as being one of the pall-bearers, and in such emotive circumstances he would have had no trouble whatever getting time off to fly down, given his Scouting position in the Colony. So why didn't he?

We think he was ordered to stay away, to make it look as if that trip down and back would be impossible for him – and so his non-attendance would cement his alibi for the coming Erroll job."

He sat back. All seven points were dangerously sharp.

"Well," he smiled, "all I've been saying is simply supposition. Have another gooseberry. But it makes a great story for the Sundays, doesn't it?"

* * *

I was horrified. Were there truly plans to print all this nonsense? It would destroy my innocent parents, who were well into their long-awaited quiet retirement, none too healthy after too many years in the tropics, and who prized their privacy far more than the CMG that Dad never got. Oxdon was watching for my reaction.

"Oh yes," he said. "It will all be published. Unless – "

"This is blackmail." I bit hard into my gooseberry as he gave me that brittle smile.

"I suppose so," he agreed coolly, "But you see, we must continue to have those Life assurance proposal-forms, just the copies, you understand."

"Wait, please," I pleaded. "I may well be kicked out of my company by next Easter."

He brightened. "Ah, that's absolutely fine. Our work will be complete by then, so this whole arrangement can end at that time. Splendid."

This, I supposed, was good news for me in a negative

way; but I still had to know who I was dealing with, and had been, for all those years. Was this the mysterious and well-informed Benson connection, for instance, or was Oxdon – by his own admission "the all-knowing" – from some entirely different group?

"Professor," I tried to make it sound fierce and demanding, "When I first came in today, I told you that I had been visited by the CIA, or maybe it was MI6. Either way, they warned me that Moscow wants our lists. They have explained why, and I now understand this. But you said a while ago that being dragged into politics was the last thing you wanted – "

"I think not. I was talking about you. We, as it happens, are deeply into politics – "

"But I have to know, don't you see, who is behind you and your use of the data. It's getting out of hand," I ended, feebly perhaps but inwardly beginning to seethe.

The old man sat thinking, and then surprisingly crumpled up the sheet of Quink and threw it across the room, missing the wastepaper basket but momentarily stirring the interest of the cat, who gazed across but decided it wasn't worth the bother. What was the significance of Oxdon's action, could I have gained an advantage at last? Seize the moment.

"Tell me then." I stood up defiantly and drummed up an angry shout. "Are you working with MI6 or with the CIA?" I banged a fist painfully on the joint-stool. "Is it the Kremlin or – or the East Germans? Israel?" I grabbed two more cape gooseberries, and chewed at them viciously while he gaped at me. "What do you know about Dutch? Deutsch? How about – " I fumbled furiously for the notes I'd brought with me, "how about Holywell and the Harts? Driberg? The rest of the Oxford ring? What about... er... Abbiss? Barter?? Binns??? Bonnett????"

He was still blinking at me with his mouth open. And well he might: the first few names were well-known Communist suspects, but the rest were straight off the top of my troubled head, drawn from my memory of my old Fourth Form register. But I could see that he suspected something of the sort. No fool, then, old Oxdon.

"How about the rest of the alphabet? Xerxes? Yashimoto?"

Suddenly he erupted into laughter, shaking all over. The cat had sensibly vanished, and his daughter came to the door to make sure he wasn't having a seizure. Maybe he was. I nearly was as well, and sat down breathless, while his shoulders still heaved.

Still twitching slightly, and wiping his eyes with a grey-looking handkerchief, he spluttered: "This has nothing to do with spying, dear boy. We aren't remotely interested in students."

From 'Too Long in the Business' by Tim Topps (Matador)

After I had written about that meeting with Oxdon, I had cause to think back.

To my astonishment, and considerable initial alarm, everything I had recorded him as saying about my parents at the time of the Erroll removal, was in real life perfectly true. Thinking of course that I had been making it all up, it slowly dawned on me that I had given the Professor a whole lot of valid facts; I realised that it must have come out of my subconscious. So I bought the four main books about the Erroll murder, and amazingly a totally unexpected but very likely fact dawned. I deal with it here, under "Matters Arising", and I sincerely hope the Boy Scout Movement will forgive me. Dad, too, as I say at the end.

* * *

My parents with the Mayor of Nairobi at the Aga Khan's birthday party

'Too Long in the Business' then summarises:

THE 'REMOVAL' OF LORD ERROLL IN 1941:
Matters arising

Happy Valley 'Personal Revenge' or a regrettable wartime necessity? And could the required finger on the trigger really have been my peace-loving, God-fearing but patriot father?

a) *PERSONAL REVENGE?*

Of the four available books on the subject, three concentrate on the Happy Valley crowd and their sleazy social antics, which of course makes a good salacious read and can bring tidy royalties. The assumption is that somebody in that group wanted Lord Erroll dead for reasons of his or her own; and there are plenty of interesting candidates. But in every case one has to ask: were any of these sad people truly murderous by nature? Or even subject to such terrible jealousy when they had all been happily sleeping with each other for years?

And if so (and there was one such lady, trigger-happy, suicidal, self-harming, and American as well), why go to the discomfort of doing it in the small hours, in the rain, in the pitch darkness of the Plains in the wartime blackout, even if you are barmy, when it could be done just as easily in the daytime, in comfort, back in town where her bottles were?

These three books do touch — remotely it seems, in passing almost — on the political possibilities and Erroll's known links with Fascism; but they hurry on (almost as if under orders) to dismiss the idea as hopelessly irrelevant. That is precisely what happened, astonishingly in my view, at the start of the trial, with that inexplicable direction, from the prosecuting Attorney-General no less, to ignore any conceivable suggestion of a political motive for the killing. Why, why, why, one asks?

It almost seems as though all three writers have somehow been persuaded (I hesitate to suggest 'briefed') to emphasise the guilt of somebody in the Valley and the Muthaiga Club in order to stir up the murram dust and shield a secret security trail that would embarrassingly lead in a different direction... And the trial itself was surely a cover-up.

Nevertheless between the lines one can glean no end of information, in bits and pieces, which can be assembled to present a highly likely picture.

"In a way you could say that I did," Broughton told the 15-year-old Juanita Carberry, shortly after being found innocent. He was telling the truth, I think, and hope to demonstrate.

b) *WARTIME NECESSITY?*

Of the four books, the three referred to above: *The Murder of Lord Erroll* by Rupert Furneaux (Stevens, 1961); the better-known *White Mischief* by James

Fox (originally Jonathan Cape, 1982, plus of course the imaginative film with its wrong ending); and much more recently *The Temptress* by Paul Spicer (Simon & Schuster, 2010), sidestep the security risk of a proselytising fascist holding the post of Military Secretary in charge of Kenya's defences, when the Northern border was lined by thousands of jubilant Fascist Italian troops who had just triumphed over Abyssinia and other parts of North Africa! Not to mention the urgent need of Mussolini to achieve a Battle Honour against Britain so that he could keep up with his superior and currently victorious ally, Hitler.

But: Oh no, Erroll is British, a Lord, long ancestry, nothing to worry about, just Happy in his Valley...

However, happy indeed to relate, the fourth of these thoughtful studies, *The Life and Death of Lord Erroll,* by Ms E. Trzebinski (Fourth Estate, 2000) assumes throughout that his 'removal' was definitely achieved by our security services. I am absolutely sure she is right: the man would have been seen as a huge risk at that precarious time, by those 'in the know', even had he been a solid well-controlled family man – as a wild card, notorious for boasting both between the sheets and afterwards, he simply "had to go". (The Governor of the colony is reported to have used those very words, a year or so earlier). And right at the very top, of course, was Churchill, fearful of a major calamity that would bring nationwide despondency (as did indeed happen a little later with our loss of Singapore).

But strangely, Ms Trzebinski seems to miss her own target. Yes, her book is enormously researched: at the back are no fewer than 918 references from her 12 chapters, and then a bibliography listing over 200 books and articles, so if they are all relevant to what I'm writing here, I may be uttering complete rubbish. But I must press on because of my father...

Trzebinski gets herself deeply into the clandestine bureaucracy which she detects in the plot leading up to the assassination. Rightly, I'm sure, she dumps overboard the great shoal of red herrings from the Happy Gang, with some of them seeking notoriety in oblivion by hurling themselves on the hooks of the Press ever since 1941. (Why is it, silly nobodies do this?) But instead, she weaves a gigantic network of plotters and supporters and back-up people, all involved in the complicated tangle she seems to think necessary for Erroll's elimination, and all of them knowing that 'something was up' at least, if not who, when or where.

Whyever does she envisage such a big unwieldy operation with all those minor characters entangled in it, all for the sake of a couple of bullets on a dark night, on the Plains with nobody about? Surely nothing could be much simpler, the sort of thing that happens all the time?

Moreover, had the affair been so bureaucratic – involving dozens of people according to her 'revelatory' Sallyport Papers – by now, over 70 years later, somebody would obviously have spilled the beans, on the internet if not openly to a thirsty newspaper. Would such an army all have gone to their graves tight-lipped when the Erroll Mystery seems to be an everlasting money-spinner?

I suggest we revert to the main characters, but read them from a different angle: their earlier 1930s background, and how it interrelates.

c) *WHAT WAS REALLY GOING ON?*

Let us assume for the purpose of the exercise that Erroll's was indeed a necessary political elimination. In May 1940, with the discovery at the home of the American spy Tyler Kent of the 'Red Book' that listed all members of the Fascist 'Right Club', Churchill – newly become Prime Minister – ordered the rounding-up of all British Fascists. Erroll, known sympathiser, was the only one in a position of military power, but he was out of reach.

Now, consider the track-records of our three main characters (and incidentally, their Intelligence connections):

JOCK DELVES BROUGHTON (b.1883) was by no means a dithery old man, as sometimes presented; but still in his fifties. A Guards officer from 1902 to 1919, (which is not to be sneezed at), and invalided as a Captain, he was then for several years kept on in the regiment, note, though deskbound; and as an active officer in that position he was very likely to have had Intelligence duties: what else?

Far too senior to go on payday duties, and useless on the parade-ground with that bad leg, how better to make use of him?

On retirement he then ran his family estate but he was also for many years a magistrate, which is seldom mentioned but puts a somewhat different slant on his capabilities. He owned land in Kenya in the early Thirties or before. And by then, we are told, he knew Hugh Dickinson.

DIANA CALDWELL (b.1913) was one of the free, adventurous, liberated girls of the 1930s. (We should not forget the many feisty young women we were dropping into occupied Europe soon after). She flew her own plane all over the place, and, note this, we are told she was already well-known to MI5 and MI6. She is said to be socially chatting-up the Vice-Chancellor of Austria, no less, shortly before Hitler's invasion: whatever for? To whom was she reporting back, working under this exciting glamorous cover? More to the point, she knew Hugh Dickinson in 1935, around the time she met Broughton.

HUGH DICKINSON (b.1906) was a Regular officer in the 9th Lancers (which, *as only I am likely to realise,* may be highly significant). He crops up everywhere in the Broughton/Diana saga, and it is easy to deduce from most of the books, not just Trzebinski, that it is he who knits the whole plot together. Consider:

31

1. If he knew them both separately in 1935, he probably introduced them socially, or was ordered to do so.

2. When they set off for South Africa in mid-1940 (and by the way, how did they get permits and book passages at that time unless they were on a mission? A few months later, no lawyer was able to go out from the UK to act for Broughton, even for £5,000!), Dickinson was close at hand. He told people he had requested a transfer to Kenya to be near Diana because he loved her so much! What eyewash! This was hardly justification for a 'compassionate posting' even in peacetime, and quite ridiculous with a major war on. He probably thought he was making a joke until he found that people believed his amateur cover story.

3. Dickinson's transfer has confused our authors a little: he was moved across to the Royal Signals? Royal Engineers? RASC? Three books, three versions; but all agree that he was only on attachment, and remained basically a 9th Lancer. Bear that in mind.

4. In Durban, finding that Kenya was barring entry to single women, Dickinson arranged the marriage of Diana and Jock (if it was genuine) and the new passports; to have made an application for Diana to be allowed to enter, exceptionally, unmarried, would no doubt have attracted unwanted newspaper attention to all three of them. And yet, belatedly, without

knowledge of the marriage, and inexplicably, unless he knew what was planned, the Governor of Kenya sent a message: "Let them all come." Why?

5. Our Lancer subaltern then turns up in Nairobi but keeps in the background, hovering on the Valley periphery 'because of his great love'. However, on the fatal night he is well out of the way, either laid-up down in Mombasa with an alibi and a poisoned leg, according to one report, or equally laid-up in a rest-home suspiciously close to the scene of the crime with a nervous twitch and an alternative alibi. (Was the truth ever established?) But in the latter case, why is he said to have had thick mud on his boots next morning? He doesn't half get around, does Dickinson, lancing about everywhere.

    And a couple of weeks after the killing, all three of them go off for an eight-day safari: the abandoned husband, his separating wife distraught at the loss of "the only man she ever loved"; Oh, and Dickinson.

    It seems howlingly obvious, doesn't it, that Diana and Jock, recruited by the ubiquitous Dickinson, never really married. (Later in life she told a friend she never intended to). They never shared a room, even for appearances' sake; they never seem to have shown any sign of real affection, despite being very recent 'newly-weds'.

    This was simply presented as the most likely set-up to attract Erroll; and the moment they got to

33

Nairobi, Diana laid it on thick, homing in on Erroll at once: almost indecently fast. Of course she didn't for a moment love Erroll, she had come to help kill him. (Apparently she had affairs with other men on the boat going out). Looking back at it all, one almost feels sorry for the man.

The Governor, we have seen, was clearly involved, *ex officio.* I reckon the Lady Mayor of Nairobi was also in the picture: the Broughtons went straight to her the moment they arrived and were with her for both lunch and dinner that first day. And then, on the crucial morning, and as soon as Erroll's death was announced, the Mayor rushed to the mortuary to look at the body, and asked to have his identity tag: whatever for, was she checking to make sure the right Happy Womaniser had been nailed? In court, she appeared hostile to Broughton for no apparent reason, but presumably this was an act to cover her tracks, knowing he would be acquitted and with an eye on her political future. (Which went very well, incidentally!)

By the time of the trial, it seems certain that the judiciary knew all about the truth, and the shocking instruction from the Attorney General to rule out any suggestion of a political motive, takes the breath away. Here we have a blatant attempt to drag the Happy Valley into the dock, alone.

And the police were in on it, too. Arthur Poppy, the CID chief, had been brought to Kenya specifically to set up a fingerprinting service a few years earlier (I met him at his office, with my Dad, in 1935 or maybe 36 and he took my prints as a joke – I think they laughed that I was the first person to have his prints on file in Nairobi – I wonder if they're still there?); but he didn't ask for any prints on Erroll's car until hours later, after the car had been towed away and thoroughly cleaned. Nor was the area around the scene roped off, so that any telltale car-tracks were soon useless. Also, note this, Poppy stopped young Juanita Carberry from giving evidence.

What else? How about the Defence Counsel? We are asked to believe that no barrister could come from the UK "because there was a war on". But it had been OK for the Broughton trio to sail out a few months earlier. I suspect that the excellent Henry Morris KC in South Africa had already been lined up for the job, no doubt by Dickinson, so that Diana's rush down to him was a bluff. How otherwise could such a successful lawyer be so swiftly available, even for £5,000? And was it normal to agree a fixed fee in advance of such a trial, unless one already knew the outcome was almost certain and the case wasn't going to run on too long?

When the main prosecution case turned on identification of the gun, wherever it was, an enormous amount of time and energy was clearly going to be quite pointless. Reading the transcript, one can vividly sense that the matter was going nowhere; and that Morris knew it, right from the start. You can't help feeling that the Prosecution knew it too, and this simply adds to the impression that the entire trial was an extended sham – which would account for Broughton's relaxed air throughout.

So, when he 'confessed' a few days later to young Juanita that he was guilty, after all, "in a way", he was – in a way – unburdening himself. Agreed, he never left the house, but he set up the shooting. He knew Erroll's exact movements, and when he called at June Carberry's bedroom door, possibly twice either side of 3 a.m., wasn't he almost certainly making a phone-call with last-minute instructions, as well as establishing his own alibi.

But phoning to whom?

Dickinson, the man of the double alibis (and muddy boots!), would be one's first choice, except that as 'an Officer and a Gentleman' he was regarded, or regarded himself, as too valuable an operative. Further, as is so often the case, the Service – whichever Service was at the root of the scheme – would want to use somebody as their liquidator who, if things went wrong, could have been cast to the wolves, with an incriminating alternative motive, in order to let the Government off the hook. Oxdon makes this clear to me at our meeting, in his slur about my war-deserted mother being chatted-up in Erroll's office (see previous chapter).

And that brings in my Dad.

d) *WAS MY FATHER THE RELUCTANT HITMAN?*

1. We went out to Kenya in 1934, when I was six. Dad had always been deeply involved in the Scouting world (as Oxdon says) and pursued this as his main off-duty interest alongside his day job as HM Assistant Trade Commissioner for KUT and Zanzibar. He formed his Rover group at once, I think, because in 1935 when Baden Powell visited Nairobi, they lined up at the station to greet him, I remember. (BP was very chatty to me afterwards, and I recall being fascinated by his telling me that his father had been born even before Napoleon came to power! I also remember that shortly afterwards, I had a weird vision of a baby in a wooden pram – tumbril? – in a crowd of old women knitting, and heads messily rolling towards me: it was all happening on my bedroom wall, and I was malarial. There were a few Henry Moore things in there too, which was worse). What my conversation with Oxdon left unsaid is that Dad soon built up a powerful strike-group drawn from his Rovers (he was made Rover Commissioner for East Africa by BP) in their late teens or early twenties, to act as a covert support for the Kenya Special Police, in many of their night-time raid operations, rounding-up suspects and known ne'er-do-wells in the settlements around Nairobi. I think this group was largely disbanded in 1939 or soon after, as so many of these youngsters went into the Forces. But I'm sure the Police files will bear me out.

2. Dad himself, however, continued to work alongside the police – and at a high level, apparently, because when I was back at school in England, some time in the early 1940s (I have the letter somewhere), he wrote describing an occasion out on the Athi Plains at night when he was 'on a job' in a car with the Chief of Police and they had been rammed by another car and overturned, rolling down a slope and covered in battery-acid. His letter ended: "This won't be in the papers!"

3. Above all else, my father was a patriot. Born in Agra as a son of the Regiment, and then educated at the Regimental School in Potchefstroom soon after the end of the Boer War, he continued moving with his SQMS father wherever the Ninth Lancers (Hugh Dickinson's regiment, note) were posted, ending in Dublin during the Irish 'troubles'. Both he and his father treasured their regimental link (Grandad's endless reminiscences about the 'red-and-yellow Ninth' during the school holidays used to entertain me, then drive me mad). Dad's approach from Dickinson, suddenly in Africa and in perilous wartime with a secret proposition, would have been almost irresistible.

4. Unlike me, my father was very much an Action Man: muscular, stocky, ginger and hairy. He was also a good shot. I remember one day when Mum and Dad were out, I was prowling around their bedroom in our house on Chiromo Road (now Riverside Drive, they tell me, or

something else in Swahili) and finding a gun under his pillow. It was a .32, I forget the make, though I pinched a couple of cartridges to show the boys at school, but they weren't very interested as all their parents also had guns under their pillows, which surprised me because in those pleasant pre-war days it hardly seemed at all necessary, at any rate to an eight-year-old. When I returned the bullets, he cuffed me on the head, but only gently. He had bought the gun secondhand when we docked at Port Said on the way out in 1934, while I was getting my topee at Simon Artz, as one did in those days. Because it was an old gun, it doubtless had the black powder which the Court would be so excited about.

5. He also had his .38 Service revolver, a Webley I expect, handed down from his own father and dating back to – at least – 1914, when Grandad had been commissioned and put in charge of a big assembly of Indians because he knew their lingo. (When their end-of-the-week parade was delayed they used to chant – and I can't spell it – "Jildi jildi all the week, but peechi peechi payday"). Dad kept the Webley until he retired back in the UK in 1960, and handed it in to the police. I remember that I remonstrated with him, because I wanted to keep it as a family heirloom, but he was, as usual, scrupulously law-abiding. But I also asked him about that little under-the-pillow .32. He told me: "Oh, I dropped that in the Nile when I was at Khartoum and we went shooting crocodiles."

6. Quite recently I happened upon an old tattered notebook, filled in pencil with Dad's diary notes of his and Mum's journey home to England in 1944, down the Nile by train, bus and riverboat, prior to waiting around the delta for a convoy ("a bit tricky passing Malta"). Most of it is just general frustration about the food, the delays, the missed connections; but a couple of the entries might have some significance in this attempt to understand Dad's possible role in the Erroll affair, so long overdue.

(a) He has meetings in Cairo with "Stirling". Now, by this date the famous Stirling was in Colditz, but his position had been taken over by his brother, who was based in Cairo.

(b) He notes that an RAF officer named Jewell, who had been his colleague in Khartoum when he was Adjutant there, is "just back from Turkey". But Turkey was neutral in early 1944, swaying between support of the Allies or the Nazis, and secretly meeting Churchill in 1943, so does this suggest covert activities and that Dad was linked to under-cover people?

(c) He writes of shooting crocodiles with his .38 Webley, so it does seem that he no longer had the .32, as he told me.

7. The aftermath is probably the most revealing aspect of this possible involvement of my Dad in the Erroll affair, together with Oxdon's 'seven points'. Facts unknown to previous writers include:

(a) The pall-bearer mystery. Since Dad was actually listed as a pall-bearer for Baden-Powell, in the newspaper the day after the funeral, it must prove that it had been a last minute cancellation. Doesn't this suggest that the Erroll action was being deliberately delayed until BP's imminent death, but then required immediately, as Dad would have wanted to insist upon?

(b) Mum often used to say that Dad had "changed somehow" in the early 1940s, and she put it down to that crash when the car rolled over (I wish I could find Dad's letter, to check on the date). He wasn't ever morose, in fact wherever they were posted over the next twenty years – Canada, Rhodesia, New Zealand, Nigeria and finally Trinidad – he continued to be much in demand as a brilliant after-dinner speaker, full of wit and much-liked by all, the various Government Houses included. But at home, away from all that, there was a quietly pensive withdrawal. And not once, ever, did he mention Erroll, throughout a twenty-year retirement; when Mum chattered away from time to time, he just 'turned off ' rather than join in.

(c) Stranger still, despite his enthusiasm since early teenage in the Scout Movement and his really close connections, once they left Kenya he never again had any contact with Scouting, none at all I believe.

8. There is a final note, just emerged, which may well be significant:
    Jack Bingham (the real-life inspiration for 'George Smiley') as a young man joined MI5 in 1940 with the specific brief to keep a close eye on UK's high society Fascists. In a recent article, his daughter remembers her shock at some of the well-known names she heard (while sitting on the stairs, I imagine). Bingham, too, was a 'son of the regiment', his father the sixth Baron having been a Lancer.

9. Summing up, this whole crowd of pointers, many known only to me it seems, has led me to think that my father must be pretty high on the list of candidates for the actual shooting. I never had a chance to ask him, of course, and anyway I don't think I would have done. After two strokes in the 1970s had put him into a bizarre but comfortable Home in Oxfordshire for those with mental deterioration (the delightful old Doctor who owned the place, making silly mistakes at his desk, said: "You know, I'm only two steps behind them all"),

Dad didn't know me on my last visit in 1980. With a big smile of happy non-recognition, he said: "Hello, are you going up-country?" He was back in Kenya at last and perhaps I was one of his Rovers.

If it was Dad's finger on that trigger, he was a staunch patriot acting under orders, and he could be relied on to keep a secret. And if now, after nearly seventy-five years, it turns out that I am divulging it, I remind myself that he always told me to tell the truth – when the time was ripe.

A letter to my aunt, from a friend in Kenya - just one reflection of public opinion at the time.

"I think the Earl of Errol's case will come out all right, & more than likely some one will hang for it, though the popular feeling seems to be he ought to get a medal for it."

III

Now things become more interesting…

In 2014, my book *Too Long in the Business* came out, with a well-distributed 'Advance Information' and 'Press Release', both of them making adequate mention of the likelihood of involvement of my Dad and – more newsworthy surely – the Chief Scout himself. It also drew attention to the practical certainty that, as I had written somewhere, the books connecting Erroll's death to the Happy Valley crowd were 'a shoal of red herrings', very likely encouraged by the authorities in order to muddy the water. I was pleased with my metaphor, probably not original; but the response to my book amazed me…

Not a word. Nary a review. Not even a phone-call. The silence was complete.

So I made some direct approaches to the national newspapers, and Hey Presto! – a result.

The features editor of the Daily Mail sent me a very friendly journalist, who drafted with me a two-page spread including photos. The Features Editor emailed me a copy of it and promised publication, he said, hopefully at an early date because it was "a favourite of my Editor". It seems that opportunities came and went, for nearly a year.

Then, without ever telling me why, the feature was suddenly spiked, if that's still the jargon (I was last an editor in 1948). Twice I tried to ask the reason, but got no reply. Now I've been told, months later, that there had simply been an editorial committee decision – but if so, why shilly-shally for a year?

Very recently, before preparing this little memoir, I tested the water again – it's still deeply murky. Just before Christmas 2015 I sent an e-mail to *all* the nationals (no, I won't flatter them with a capital 'N') telling them that I was planning an article which would contain my latest findings; I included the same message in with my latest book (on things quite different) to a dozen Book Editors. I pointed out that my revelations could well be published on the actual 75th anniversary of Erroll's death, 24 January. Was this of any interest, I asked.

Not a single word from any of them. Not even saying "No, thanks."

So here it is...

WINSTON SENDS IN THE CAVALRY ... ?

It seems clear to me that other writers about the Erroll affair have given insufficient thought to Churchill's frightful predicament. Yes, they go on about the Italians crowding Kenya's north border, and the German mutterings down in Tanganyika; but put yourself in his position...

You become, on 10 May 1940, Prime Minister of a Cabinet many of whom don't like you, while the rest have often in recent years distrusted you; among those around the table, quite a few believe we must (not should, but *must*) plead for a humiliating deal with Hitler in order to avoid the swift horror that has in recent weeks swept across so much of mainland Europe. While you sit and discuss this, your Army in France is being tumbled into the sea at Dunkirk (where no rescue has yet been considered possible); the enormous air Armada of the Luftwaffe is soon ranged up along the Continental coasts with orders to destroy our airfields and aircraft as a prelude to the inevitable invasion...

In the terrifying midst of this, suddenly on 20 May when you have hardly got your legs under your new desk, your Chief of MI6, Sir Stewart Menzies, tells you that in the flat of a renegade American Embassy clerk has been found 'the Red Book' listing hundreds of prominent Britons who belong to the British Union of Fascists. What do you do – and remember, you're already a bit busy (there's a war on) ... ?

What Churchill did was delegate. Under super-spycatcher John Bingham the BUFs were all quickly rounded-up, together with some unlisted Associates. All but one: Erroll was out of reach. But under the dire East African circumstances he was perhaps the most dangerous of all, having got himself appointed to a top position in Kenya's defences... And there was Mussolini on the warpath, for some years the benefactor of the British Union of Fascists, quite apart from his other interests!

Who is Winston going to turn to, to sort out this Erroll? The clue must lie in his own background, and one can detect the answer by looking at the backgrounds of nearly all the people who actually became involved in the Erroll affair. Of course we have Stewart Menzies of the Secret Service, an ex-Life Guard officer, but he was on the spot already and may have given Winston the idea. But next there is Bingham (prototype for fictional spycatchers) rounding up those accessible Fascists – his father was a Lancer. Then note the leading character who is tasked with the actual up-close Kenya operation, Delves Broughton, many years in the Irish Guards, but long confined to a desk-job after a leg accident, so most likely in Intelligence (because what else?). We have Major Dicky Pembroke (lately of the Coldstream Guards), a shadowy figure who had been at the Muthaiga Club since early in the war – why? – and incidentally was transferred to Cairo as soon as Broughton was released. There's something odd about Pembroke: the White Mischief index usually gives a brief remark after each page entry for the main characters – even Morris, Poppy and Soames –

but under Pembroke just a bald list of page numbers. And Trzebinski does likewise. Then the ubiquitous Dickinson (and with that appropriate adjective perhaps he ought to have claimed as his cover just The Royal Engineers rather than Signals and Service Corps!) but in fact he was a Ninth Lancer. As, via his father and as a 'son of the regiment', was my Dad.

You will concede, I hope, that Churchill could hardly have organized all this himself at a time when the Channel was full of little boats and the skies full of wheeling death, let alone our fortunes swinging sweatily to and fro in the sands of North Africa. So again, he delegated. But to whom?

Churchill himself had been a cavalryman, a Hussar, in the Boer War. And also a Hussar had been Baden-Powell. Further (and this has not been spotted by any 'Erroll mystery' writer, I believe), Baden-Powell in the early 1900s was appointed the UK Inspector of Cavalry.

He was now living outside Nairobi and he would have known them all.

More to the point in this memoir, he knew and admired my Dad's Special Police work, also the proud Ninth Lancer connection, and most probably told Dickinson.

As one would.

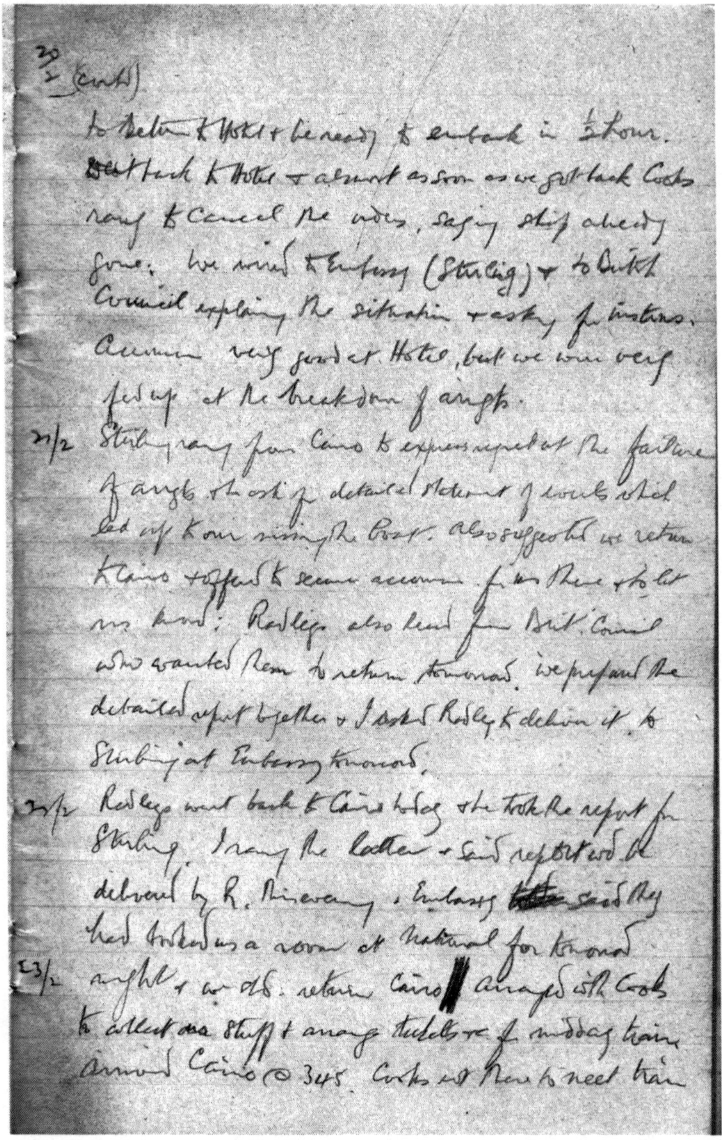
20/2 (contd)
to return to Hotel & be ready to embark in ½ hour.
Went back to Hotel & almost as soon as we got back Cooks
rang to cancel the order, saying ship already
gone. We wired to Embassy (Stirling) & to British
Council explaining the situation & asking for instructions.
Accomm. very good at Hotel, but we were very
fed up at the breakdown of arrgts.
21/2 Stirling rang from Cairo to express regret at the failure
of arrgts & to ask for detailed statement of events which
led up to our missing the boat. Also suggested we return
to Cairo & offered to secure accomm. for us there & to let
us know. Radleys also heard from Brit. Council
who wanted them to return tomorrow. We prepared the
detailed report together & I asked Radley to deliver it to
Stirling at Embassy tomorrow.
22/2 Radleys went back to Cairo today & he took the report for
Stirling. I rang the latter & said report would be
delivered by R. this evening. Embassy [redacted] said they
had booked us a room at National for tomorrow
23/2 night & we sh'd return Cairo [redacted] arranged with Cooks
to collect our stuff & arrange tickets etc for midday train
Arrived Cairo @ 3.45. Cooks sent there to meet train

Dad's tattered notebook

Because he was obviously very frail, in his eighties, and having many periods of alarmingly bad health, Baden-Powell's participation in the planning of Erroll's removal does not seem to have been examined by anybody: understandably, since he died before the shooting.

But as I have shown, this was the ideal person for Churchill to turn to: UK's former Inspector of Cavalry, living on the spot, time on his hands, knowing all the right people, high and low, and utterly patriotically trustworthy. Moreover, when the alarm-bells first rang back in May 1940 he was fully active and reasonably hale and hearty. I have letters he wrote in those times to my father and they are not just coherent but well-thought-through, and in a firm hand, though later, towards the Autumn, he dictates them to Olave (Lady Baden-Powell). Yet I learn from Tim Jeal's monumental biography (Yale University Press 2001) that he was still painting water colours and designing the traditional Christmas card in October. The final downhill slide only began on 8 November 1940, and even then there were frequent rallies. BP would have been keeping in touch right up to the Broughtons' arrival, on November 12.

Other curious snippets now begin to bring Olave, Lady BP, into the picture, as she seems most anxious to keep herself out of it. Her autobiography is naturally full, for hundreds of pages, of everything to do with her husband. But his funeral is dismissed in just eight lines – and she didn't attend it! It was an important affair, as one may well imagine: all the top people of Kenya were there and many others besides. The pall-bearers included Lord Erroll – and my father! – but Dad excused himself (because he was away in Khartoum, he had said, though it would have been easy enough to get leave in view of his Rover Commissioner position; I've already dealt with this). Olave evidently knew what was going on, and perhaps she felt quite unable to chat socially with a man whom she knew was to be killed next week, due to her husband's involvement ? If this is so, it is perfectly understandable.

Erroll's name doesn't even appear in those pages of her book. But Olave must have had other misgivings about the whole episode and maybe BP shared them? At the beginning of her book she prints a whole family tree dating back to the 17th century, where her Scottish family name is Hay. Erroll's Scottish family name, though a different tree, is also Hay. That must have been worrying enough.

But also on her tree are many Soameses – Soames was her maiden name. And when Delves Broughton arrives on November 12 1940 with the new wife he wasn't sleeping with (they had apparently 'married' on 5 November but there evidently hadn't been any fireworks), he goes straightaway to spend a week with an old chum who has a farm outside Nairobi, leaving his newlywed Diana free to work her dubious magic on Erroll.

The old chum? Jack Soames, (Cavalry Reserve, 1914).

DID MY FATHER REALLY FIRE THOSE SHOTS?

$\int$ omeone did. And I am confident that it was someone other than a Happy Valley nut. It was a necessary defence measure at a crucial time of war, and I believe I have put forward sufficient evidence – albeit circumstantial – to place Dad pretty high up on the list; after all, what other names are there? We know that Broughton was not physically equipped for the job. Dickinson? He was too exposed and over-obvious, surely, cropping up everywhere in various uniforms and muddy boots, being in two different places on the crucial night: it all reads like the scenario for a Philip Marlowe prime suspect, astonishingly innocent on the last page.

So, in the absence of any other contender, let me summarise my suspicions, including those which have emerged from my deeper researches *after* my book was published in 2014. I will probably be repeating myself in the summary, but remember I am 89 – and anyway, isn't that what summaries do?

Dad didn't attend BP's funeral as a pall-bearer as was intended (official reason: he was away in Khartoum). Real reason: he had to shoot Erroll, another pall-bearer, next week, when he was being flown down and back very simply by the RAF. Nothing must implicate the Scouts or BP personally. Also, if things went wrong, and Erroll survived (he would probably be armed) he would have made the BP pall-bearer connection.

Not only BP but the Chief of Police and the Governor

all knew of Dad's and his Rovers' after-hour activities. But nobody else did, presumably. Then Dickinson (Ninth Lancer) turns up, and undoubtedly is directed to my (Ninth Lancer, devoted son-of-the-Regiment) father.

As my mother worked in Erroll's office and he had been chatting-her-up, here was a useful escape for the plotters if things went wrong. They would claim the shooting was a personal matter of revenge, I suppose, and the Government would be off the hook. But it didn't go wrong, and as a result of Dad's success on the night we now appear to have a complete security blanket. Suffocating my book, as I've told you!

Dad never continued, and rarely even mentioned, his 25 years of Scouting in all his later postings. On arrival as UK Trade Commissioner there were always interviews with the local newspapers, but when asked about his off-duty interests he merely said that in Kenya he had worked with the Special Police.

At home, though in every other way as bright and witty as ever, he never mentioned the Erroll affair, although it was still a major talking-point when wartime Kenya came up in conversation. Mum would chatter on about it, but Dad would seem to go quiet, change the subject, or even find an excuse to go and let the cat out or check the heating. All this, of course, comes back to my memory long after.

Some more things have come back as well: when I was in the sixth-form I had a card at school from Olave Baden-Powell, whom I'd never before heard from, inviting me to tea at her grace-and-favour flat at Hampton Court.

I was deep into studying for my Higher School Cert (i.e. A-levels) and in two minds, so I asked Dad, who was then back in the UK on leave (I hadn't seen my parents for seven years!). He advised me not to go "because of these doodle-bugs". But we had all learnt to carry on with our lives despite the odd motorbike noises from the sky above. Was his real reason the possibility that in her old age, Olave might let some cat out of her – and Dad's – bag?

And another thing which only dawned on me a few weeks ago. In my book I mention Dad handing-in their two guns after they retired to the UK, his Army .38 and her .25 Browning. But, scraping my old memory once again, I now recall this happening at Cambridge Police, not in Sussex where they retired first in 1960. They moved to a village near me, briefly, in 1976 before going into a Retirement Home. The firearm laws, as we know, are strict, so whyever were they permitted to keep those pistols for sixteen years?

* * *

Throughout the 1950s-60s the splendid Whitaker's Almanack listed the names of all our Empire-wide UK Trade Commissioners and I have been skimming through them on the shelves of The Bodleian (not bad as one's local library). They numbered about thirty, based at various vantage-points, and their postings, shifted about though they were, usually lasted for a couple of three-year tours: time to get abreast of the local opportunities for British exporters but moving on before getting stale.

Dad, though, seems to have moved far more often and always to a potential trouble-spot. After that home-leave in 1944 he was posted to Ottawa which was later found to be awash with Communist spies (Grandad and I saw him off from Euston in an air-raid); by 1947-8 he was in Rhodesia where unilateral breakaway was simmering; Nigeria/Gold Coast/Gambia is recorded next, a dangerous melting-pot and rather unhealthy physically when you are over 50 (his Assistant died soon after arriving in Lagos); ending up in the Caribbean, a laid-back final posting one might think, Trinidad and Tobago, but the islands were in the throes of independence and there could be trouble...

But in between, and not even listed in Whitaker, he had been posted to New Zealand, for just a year, when the young Queen Elizabeth was paying a visit. Is there something I still don't know about my Dad?

And does the Umzindusi letter tell me?

Dad in Trinidad 1958 as HM Trade Commissioner
greeting Princess Margaret

Dad and Mum in retirement in Sussex

IV

OUT FROM UNDER THE SECRECY BLANKET: POSITIVE EVIDENCE AT LAST?

I have always felt that if my father had been persuaded (perhaps by Baden-Powell, and certainly by Dickinson) to carry out the shooting, he must have insisted on conditions.

Being 'under orders' after having volunteered for the RAF in 1940, he was in no position to refuse this alarming assignment; but there were 'wheels within wheels' associated with the essential protection of the good name of the Boy Scouts Movement, and of Baden Powell himself, which he must have realised, and seized upon.

So, remembering my father, I can envisage the following conditions upon which he must have insisted, surely with old BP's agreement since they knew each other well, socially.

FIRST OF ALL: no hint whatever of BP's or the Scout Movement's involvement. This was an absolute priority: Scouting at that time was spreading throughout the world as a Peace Movement embracing all races and classes. I have a letter to Dad from BP, praising the new development in Kenya of Groups and Packs of whites, Indians and native Africans without any discrimination (though he's not so sure about the Arabs), very advanced thinking for that time. So there must be no smear on Scouting. Now or at any time in the future.

SECOND: If things go wrong – Dad would have realized that, in that unfortunate event, he would be 'on his own'. He must provide for this. His wife, my Mum would be covered by their generous Civil Service pension, so no worry there. But how about his only son – me? This is where it gets interesting and the Umzindusi letter comes into the picture.

* * *

In late 2015, sifting through some of Dad's old files which I had never before found, there was a crumpled old OHMS envelope containing a few yellowing pages held together by a rusty Civil Service pin: it took me half-an-hour to separate them without doing myself an injury. I was then about to dismiss them until I noticed the dates: all were early 1941.

There were four letters. The first, from Dad to the Foreign Office on airmail paper, was an application for me, age 13, to sit for the Consular Scholarship exam, which was an annual prize open by competition to the children of the UK's Foreign and Colonial officers. It was sent from him in Khartoum, just a few days after Erroll's shooting.

Letters two and three as I looked at them were encouraging missives from two of Dad's superior officers. The first of these, in the Spring of 1941, strangely tells him in very friendly terms that I stand a very good chance of winning the scholarship because it doesn't necessarily go to the one with the highest results. Other factors are taken into account, he adds rather mysteriously.

Then there comes, a bit later, a letter from his other boss, when I have in fact won the Scholarship. He writes (very kindly, I have to admit with hindsight) that I have won the Scholarship fair-and-square, and "though this must be confidential", he encloses the actual scores in each subject, of the top three entrants, to prove it. But, you see, he only felt the need to do this because he knew that Dad was being rewarded, through my scholarship, for something else.

* * *

That 'something else' seems to be confirmed by the final letter. Final not in date (it came at the end of March) but in the sense that, I believe, it finalises all the speculation about the Erroll shooting.

My Grandad received the succinct message at his Umzindusi home in Tadworth. It simply reads: "I am instructed by Mr Winston Churchill to confirm that" I had been entered for the Consular Scholarship. And on Foreign Office, not Downing Street, paper.

Yes, but look more closely at the end of March 1941. It was again one of the most devastating weeks of the war, when such a huge tonnage of crucial shipping was lost to U-boats that our island's survival was at its highest-ever risk. Winston must have been frantic underneath the outward calm. Whyever would he – could he, of all people – spend even a minute writing about a petty matter like a boy's entry for a scholarship...?

Unless it was important. The Umzindusi letter is dated two days after Delves Broughton was arrested and charged.

The job was done. Dad was in the clear. The agreed reward was forthcoming.

* * *

In any further communication on this subject, please quote
No. K 3117/2504/250.

and address—
not to any person by name
but to—
"The Under-Secretary of State,"
Foreign Office,
London, S.W.1.

FOREIGN OFFICE.

S.W.1.
25th March, 1941.

Sir,

In reply to your letter of the 19th March, I am directed by Mr. Winston Churchill to inform you that the candidature of your grandson, Alan J. Broad, for this year's Consular Service Scholarship has been accepted.

A busy week for Mr Churchill. Nevertheless, a letter was sent about a boy's scholarship.

* * *

I write as Tim Topps but my real name is Alan Broad and my father was Daniel Broad of HM Trade Commissioner Service (b.1900 in Agra - d.1981 in Wardington, near Banbury), a gentle man loved by all.

* * *

Message from The Chief Scout

I RECEIVED the cablegram from the Commissioners and Secretaries Conference only some days after it had been dispatched and so was unable to reply in time to catch the meeting. I should like, however, (through THE SCOUTER or otherwise) to thank them and to tell them how deeply touched I was for their kindly thought of me and how grateful for their kind message.

I am trying to carry out the eleventh Scout Law, but it is difficult to do when everybody is so enthusiastic and one gets laid up in spite of one's self.

I am having a rest cure now which I hope will set me up for the second lap of my tour which begins in February.

R̃ver Baseṇ̃Posell

GILT CROSS.

Patrol Leader L. Poole, of St. Stephens, Worcester, Troop. For his gallantry in stopping a runaway horse, attached to a cart, in Laugherne Road, Worcester, on August 11th, 1926.

H. Grebby, Scoutmaster of 2nd Ilkeston (1st Y.M.C.A.) Troop. For his gallantry in rescuing a boy from drowning in a lake at The Beauty Spot, Ilkeston, on August 24th, 1926.

D. Broad, Asst. Scoutmaster, of Southfields Methodist Troop, Wandsworth. For his gallantry in stopping a runaway horse, attached to a cart, in Durnsford Road, Wimbledon Park, on July 17th, 1926.

CERTIFICATE OF GALLANTRY.

C. Spring, Asst. Scoutmaster, and *R. Smith*, Scout, of The West Malverns Troop. For their gallant conduct, on the occasion of a drowning fatality which occurred in the River Avon at Twyning, Glos., on August 16th, 1926.

LETTER OF COMMENDATION.

First Tillmouth Troop and *First Cornhill Troop*, Cornhill and District Association. " For good work "

THAT PRECISE DATE – a military urgency?

The night of 23-24 January was the very moment that British East African and Allied forces launched an attack on the Italians along Kenya's north border. Given his position in the army, Erroll must have been fully aware of this operation, which drove up the coast of Somalia towards Mogadishu.

Lord Erroll

But this was a feint. General Cunningham's real assault came hundreds of miles inland a week later, into Ethiopia itself: a thrust through Moyale aimed at the capital Addis Ababa, and designed back in October 1940 in The Eden Plan, to coincide with the very sensitive reinstatement of the Emperor Haile Selassie. We are told that this was: "Top Secret until the very last minute" ...

Ms Trzebinski reports an overheard phone conversation of Erroll's, discussing business opportunities in Ethiopia and Eritrea (Madagascar too) when the military operation was still 'under wraps'. He was shot two days later. Was he kept 'out of the loop' because of his Fascist background and the evident looseness of his security? And finally, reluctantly, for the good of the cause and to be on the safe side, dispatched in the only way feasible?

* * *

Anthony Eden's Plan had been drawn up in late October 1940. Its main purpose was the restoration of Emperor Haile Selassie to Ethiopia, with attacks from both Sudan and General Cunningham's East African command in Kenya. The conference was in Khartoum, attended by six Generals and doubtless a lot of executives with follow-up duties, all sworn to secrecy.

My Dad had very recently been sent up to Khartoum, to be 'RAF Station Adjutant', but with the rather surprisingly lowly rank (for a 40-year-old Administrative Civil Servant of 20 years' standing) of Pilot Officer. Was this where he received his instructions about Erroll, I wonder?

And was that low rank in order to avoid too much attention in the Mess from senior officers?

LATEST RESEARCH (AT DECEMBER 2016)

1. (re. p50) Baden Powell, despite or perhaps because of his age, would have had a powerful incentive to perform this final service to the military. His four years as UK Inspector of Cavalry had been something he was 'fully unfitted for' (he wrote) and they were not happily remembered in the Army. The proud old man must have seen this as a last chance to correct matters and retrieve his splendid earlier reputation.

2. (re. p40) When Dad arrived in Cairo on his way home in 1944 the diary mentions his contacts with Stirling and meetings at 'Passport Control' in the British Embassy. The recent death of the Queen's lifelong friend Margaret Rhodes has led to extracts being published from her Memoirs; she describes being recruited early in WW2 by MI6 and posted to the section known as 'Passport Control', which dealt with Secret Agents in the Middle East...

3. (re. p57) I have so far found no record whatever in RAF lists from 1940, of Dad being commissioned. He arrived in Khartoum that autumn, straight from his Civil Service desk in Nairobi it seems, in the uniform of a somewhat superannuated Pilot Officer; but I now suspect that this was a cover and his posting was purely concerned with the imminent Eden Conference in late October, and its plans for Ethiopia which I have just mentioned. Dad returned from Khartoum a few months after the Erroll shooting and was seconded to work with OETA (Occupied Enemy Territory Administration) among the Italian colonies in the Horn.

14 Aug 40

My dear Broad

I was very glad to see your three Rovers here.

They seemed a nice, intelligent set of lads, very well & smartly turned out in their uniform. & evidently keen on their work. If they are samples of what the rest of your Rovers are like you must have a very good crew indeed — & I congratulate you. I was very interested to hear about their war work, & they told me how very keen the younger Scouts are on it too.

I was very pleased that they planned to visit the Mission troop of African boys here. It means a step in gradually over coming class & colour distinction, just as does the meeting of Indians on common ground with British boys. It has never been done till Scouting came along to suggest it. — But it means a valuable step towards the future relationship and unity of the different races in E. Africa.

Best wishes & thanks,

Yours

BP

Letter to Dad from BP, praising Scout developments

I am grateful to Nigel West for his helpfulness; to the Ninth Lancers archivist in Derby; and to Ms Trzebinski's splendid book, for many details that appear relevant; also to the artist of the immensely evocative *Lone Tree* painting, who I'm sure will be quick to tell me if it is still in copyright!

AFTERTHOUGHT

My memories of 1930s Nairobi seem to bring back a sense of general happiness which pervaded everybody; and this has nothing whatever to do with the weirdly un-Happy Valley crowd of whom, of course, at that age I knew nothing. Maybe I was too naïve to recognize troubles brewing below the surface? But then, if that is so, it must equally have hoodwinked BP, who rejoiced in the Kenya of those days, and wrote so much about it and enthused in letters to my Dad about the development of Scouting to all the local ethnic groups. And surely, he was no fool?

However unfashionable it is to say so, I often wonder how many of our ex-Empire colonies are now as well-off and (yes – why not?) as basically 'happy' as they were in the 1930s. Long ago I wrote a couple of very short stories which (as I explain in my book *The Bunny Run*) are based upon actual events from those days just before the War. I thought you wouldn't mind if I reprint them here, hoping to show you what I mean...

* * *

STATUS

From the verandah on a clear day you could see Mount Kilimanjaro – or at least, you could if your Dad lifted you up shoulder-high – and this was a favourite operation in the family because at that distance the mountain looked soft and round and comfortable, like one of Grandma's Christmas puddings back in England.

They always had breakfast on the verandah unless the weather was bad: local fruit-juice followed by Post Toastie cornflakes for him and his mother, which wasn't very adventurous, but his Dad was more experimental in his approach to the tropics, and might have mango or a big grinning slice of paw-paw or other things that looked like melon and tasted like paint.

He was eight. For him, the verandah was the hub of the house, not just their morning meeting-place. It was the back-cloth for his parties and birthday teas, and it was where he laid out his new clockwork train-set with the lead railway-porter and station-master, and the Dinky toys he had brought from home... It was also an exciting place because, though securely part of the house, it opened out on to Africa. The garden, a mere tumble of rough grass so far, sloped down to a rocky stream, then merged into the outer limits of civilized

Nairobi: scrubland where you could hear hyenas laughing or jackals snuffling around the rubbish dumps, as you lay safely under your upstairs mosquito-net at night-time; and where – so the grownups would claim over their evening whiskies on your verandah – you might spot the occasional family of lion, cautious and elusive, but still as curious as any other cat when the noises of humans attracted them... (He had heard this when friends came in for a 'sundowner', and he – supposed to be on his way to bed – was sitting on the stairs and listening).

He learnt a lot, sitting on the stairs. Grown-up conversation was of limited value but every now and then he might pick up a phrase or an opinion to be retailed at school the next day, dropped into the playtime chatter to gain him a bit of prestige. And this was very necessary, because he was so 'new': not just a new boy at school, but new to the Colony. Some of the children in his class came from old-established settler families who had been in Kenya since goodness-knew-when: 1910 or something, before the War. Many others, with parents working for the big Companies, had been born here in the twenties; but his was a Government family sent out only last year in 1935, and in that (certainly at junior schoolboy level) there was a subtle but definite inferiority... He always had to be on the alert for chances to improve his status – sitting on the stairs came to play a vital part in this.

Of course there were others in the same situation, linked in friendship by this mutual feeling of strangeness. Jan, from South Africa, was his closest boy friend. They used to cycle down into the centre of Nairobi together on Saturdays, with their 50 cents pocket-money, and go to the pictures or buy packets of foreign stamps from the little shop at the Newspaper Office opposite the War Memorial. Then they'd ride back and sit in the greenhouse, humming the songs from the Fred Astaire or Dick Powell film they'd seen...

"Smoke Gets In Your Eyes"... "I've Been Waiting for an Angel"... and asking each other what it was all about.

Then there was Lottie. At school she shared a desk with him, and that was something special and intimate, leading to all sorts of secrets which must surely be very close to the mysterious sharings his parents did at home? Lottie had come out to Kenya from Germany about the same time as he had come from England. Her father was some sort of official with a very funny accent, but her English was perfect by now, and together they tried to pick up Swahili.

It was fun, learning the words alongside your parents, being quicker at it than them, being able to call the gardener the *'shamba-boy'* and knowing what was wanted from the tool-shed when he sent you to find a 'panga' for cutting back the undergrowth. The house-boys used to call him the *'Bwana Kidogo'* which was 'The little boss' and out-and-out flattery: behind your back they had vivid and sometimes unrepeatable nicknames for you all, and usually your Dad knew about it and it was taken in good part all round... In those days there seemed a good working relationship.

He used to meet Lottie before school every morning, at the bus-stop. Now he was eight, he could go that far by himself, down the rough-made road and over the railway-crossing... Big steam-rollers were at work on the road, crushing down the sprawling heaps of *'murram'*, a red bubbly stone for road-making, not at all smooth and boring like the tarmac of London streets, but strange rounded knobs of loose crunchy stuff that had come out of volcanoes – that was another fact he had learnt while sitting on the stairs, and at school some of the big boys had spoken to him kindly after he had passed this knowledge on, one break-time.

But they all used to walk through the murrum carelessly, scuffing their feet, and of course his mother wouldn't let him do that with his new shoes, so the friendliness from the seniors had been a bit tenuous and died out by the next day.

Sometimes he got to the bus-stop first, sometimes Lottie. The level-crossing was an exciting place because you could see the massive railway-engines with their hooters and their cow-catchers like a row of shining oily teeth, as they heaved their trucks and their sleeping-cars up from Mombasa through the capital, bound for the hinterland and Lake Victoria... Vast clouds of grey smoke puffed out from the wood logs that fuelled them.

Once at night-time, coming back from school extra late for some reason, they had sat in the bus while the up-train struggled past in the darkness, wheezing like an old man, and the sky was a whirlwind of burning red sparks, weaving and shining like a swarm of fire-flies, and Lottie had grabbed his hand in wonder as they watched it go by.

As he stood waiting at the bus-stop, the long straggle of native women would come past, bearing on their heads an endless assortment of goods to market.

From hooks in their ears hung long copper bangles which swung and glinted as they walked, and many were going to get into trouble in the town when the askaris saw them, because nearly always those copper wires had been stolen from the new telegraph-poles upcountry – fashion having always had the edge on technology. But whatever the police might say or do, the women were always cheerful and glided jauntily along, chewing at long sticks of sugar-cane which they would spit out on to the side of the road when the juice had all gone, so that you could always identify a main road into Nairobi from the villages by the endless trail along its verges of dry white chewed sugar-cane.

By now, he could recognise some of the women, with their funny scarred lines and patterns on their cheeks, tribal marks which were just as natural as your mother's lipstick once you got used to the idea. And one girl in particular, in an orange frock, with a lean swinging figure and a nice face, had once smiled at him and offered him a stick of sugar-cane but he had been too shy to take it; so an older boy from a settler family got it instead... She had looked back then and smiled at him again, and he hadn't known whether to feel big or small.

It was only a short journey on the bus; then he and Lottie would take the path across a field of mealies to reach the school gates. Back in England he had never heard of mealies, and it was the shock of his life when an American boy told him it was just maize, what you make corn-flakes with, and another friend had said: "No, that is Indian Corn", but whatever it was, the very hugeness of it in the field, growing way above their heads, was always a bit awe-inspiring when he remembered the gentle Sussex cornfields he could see across at shoulder-height.

In the centre of the mealie-field stood a shabby bungalow-style farm-house, where a man lived who was Lottie's uncle. He had been there since the early days of German East Africa, and he was thin and weather-beaten and his khaki shirt and shorts hung on him much as the dry leaves hung down from the mealies... They used to call Hello to him on their way to school, hurrying past in fear of a rap across the knuckles from Miss Logan's ruler if they were late for assembly... But on the way home they would dawdle, and play "house" in the lean-to shed at the back of the old man's bungalow. It was there that he told her, one day soon after a Fred Astaire film, that he was going to marry her when they grew up; and then she had happened to find a brass curtain-ring lying on a shelf, and gave it to him to put on her finger; and after he had done that, they had agreed to keep the whole thing a secret, and together they hid the ring in a knot-hole in the wall before going for their bus. And there it stayed: always, whenever they looked to make sure.

As time went on and their friendship deepened, he used to share with Lottie any special news he had learnt on the stairs the previous evening: it was a way of showing his affection; and indeed, apart from Dinky toys which were too masculine, and caterpillars which had lost their appeal for her after one got squashed underfoot in the shed, information was the most valuable thing he had to offer. It sometimes paid off, when they bore extra-special tidings to the playground: like a very early occasion when the old King had died and Edward VIII came to the Throne, and sitting on the terrace in the January sunshine they thoughtfully told their assembled listeners how at least one good thing would come of it – certainly the Silver Jubilee stamps would go up in value...

But the new year developed badly. With the passing months, the grown-ups were changing. Gradually they seemed to lose the happiness of their chatter in the evenings on his verandah: more and more, the talk would be serious, voices lowered when they sensed him on the stairs. Once, when he was found there by Kitau the house-boy who was usually an ally, his mother was alerted and he was bundled off upstairs in almost public disgrace... This was bewildering. He could read the newspaper headlines of course, as they waved at him in the mornings across the table and the paw-paw; and he came to recognise words and comments from overheard conversations, like Rhineland, Austria, Italy, Hitler, Abyssinia... It meant very little.

But then, at school the other boys began to notice his lack of new information: he was no longer an authority on items of interest. One of the others even had to tell *him* that there had been an invasion, some time ago, of Abyssinia which was the bordering country to the North. He was losing his prestige... And if that went, since he had no particular compensating prowess at cricket, football, on the rifle-range, even in the classroom, there was a danger of his losing the devotion of Lottie. True, she had shown no sign of disaffection, but she was certainly seeming a little unhappy nowadays, and at their morning meetings one sometimes saw signs of recent tears, hints of trouble at home. He knew that a master-stroke was needed, and without delay.

That weekend, for the first time ever, he politely declined to go with his parents on their drive out to watch game on the plains. The heavy old box-body car with its big spotlight above the driver's window, would park at a likely spot near the water-holes. Zebra, buck, giraffe, and wildebeest were commonplace of course, and over the other side of town where it was even dustier, ostriches. Also, when your luck was in, you might see lion and leopards; and failing all that, there was always the four-engined biplane that arrived every Sunday with the week's mail from Croydon... A social event: meet the plane, meet your friends.

But this time, 'No Thank-you', he would like to stay in the house and do his stamps; and his parents smiled over the top of his head and thought how he was growing up and developing that charming yet hateful blasé independence we all get when we are coming up to nine. With Kitau and the shamba-boy near at hand, he would be quite all right; so off they drove for the evening, and he waved to them past the orange trees and down the red lumpy road.

Then, he went and gathered up all the newspapers he could find; he turned on the wireless to hear the News: ("Seven L.O. Nairobi Kenya calling"), and he studied Current Affairs as if a scholarship depended upon it. True, he read chiefly the headlines; but there were maps, and commentaries which he could understand, and there were captions to photographs of fierce men marching about in a

74

goose-step and feeble looking ones lying down... With his Bartholomew School Atlas open on the carpet beside him, it all began to make some sense. By the time his parents returned for supper, full of the thrill of seeing a leopard in a tree with its kill, he had his own Big Story quite clear in his head, he had tidied up the papers, and he was back on the carpet with his stamp collection.

On Monday morning at the bus-stop he told Lottie all about the world situation. She listened quietly. He was very wrapped-up in the urgency of it all, and if she sat there twisting her pigtail and biting her lip, he didn't notice. In 'break', he caught the attention of the bigger boys by commenting upon the stupidity, of any country that had to print postage-stamps for 10,000,000 marks or ten million anything; he said that if they had done that after the Great War, who knew what other dangerous things they might get up to... This wasn't challenged, so he went on to say how everybody was worried about another War coming: it was all the fault of the Germans again, they were marching into other people's countries, and killing everybody, and this was the Biggest News Ever but the grown-ups wouldn't tell the children about it, yet it was happening and soon there would be tanks again and poison gas and aeroplane dog-fights like it said in those old War Illustrated books in the library, and it was the Germans doing it all.

Most of the lunch-break he answered questions, even from some of the biggest boys. One of them walked back to the bus with him after school, and another invited him to play on Saturday. Lottie wasn't there because she had

75

been sick and gone home early... but girls are a bit stupid anyway, said the older boy.

She wasn't at the bus next morning either, and her mother had sent a message to say she was ill. But when he passed through their mealie-field that afternoon, he slipped through the fence into their special shed, and she was there: sitting in the dark, on her own, crying a little, with the brass curtain-ring on her finger...

No, she wasn't coming back to the school, she told him. She had been ordered not to talk to him again, and her uncle in the khaki shorts was terribly angry, and anyway they were going back home to Europe soon, and she thought it best if he just please took the curtain-ring and kept it to remember her by.

So he took the grubby brass ring silently from her finger. Somehow he knew that something terrible was happening, that he had helped to bring it about... but he couldn't quite work out what it was... It was like the part of a film, near the end, where everything goes wrong momentarily... but in the film it all came out right in the end.

Therefore, he thought, there can't be anything to worry about in the long run. And they agreed about that, and they promised to write and to send each other all the new stamp issues that came out – even if they are a thousand million marks, he joked – and then he got up and trudged off alone through the mealie-field without looking back, like he'd seen at the pictures with Jan.

It was late afternoon now, as he walked towards the bus-stop, and the usual native women were trailing back from market with their baskets empty on their heads.

He felt an unusual kind of loneliness as he clutched his brass ring, a sense that somehow things were changing... He knew that the day was coming, when he could no longer be a listener sitting on the stairs, but would have to join the grown-ups who occupied his verandah in the evenings, would have to share not only their sun-downers but all the worries of their world, too...

The slender young woman in the orange frock had sold her load of bananas, and came smiling past. As she reached him, they looked at each other and she stopped for a moment, seeing distress in his eyes.

"Jambo", she said – Hello – and held out a piece of sugar-cane. This time he took it without hesitation. Then he noticed that she had lost the copper bangles from her ears.

"Jambo", he replied, and he opened his hand to her with the curtain-ring in it.

With a big grin she took it from him. "Santa sana", she said – Thank you – and putting it to her ear she swung away towards her village.

He strolled on, up the dusty road with his satchel, spitting out sugar-cane and scuffing his new shoes in the murram like anything.

* * *

Memorial Hall, Nairobi

LONE TREE

It wasn't a particularly far-flung corner of the Empire: East Africa was fairly well-known and accessible in the 1930s, or at any rate the large towns. You could get to Nairobi by Imperial Airways in their great lumbering biplanes, or more likely make a proper holiday of it and take the Union Castle boat that sailed out with such clockwork regularity: "Every Friday at 4 o'clock," wasn't it, they used to advertise? A splendid business trip for visiting VIPs, out through Suez, buying your topee at Simon Artz emporium as you passed Egypt; then back round the Cape, and all on the tax-payer or the share-holder. There was no shortage of volunteers from Home, to attend any special celebration in Nairobi, unless of course it happened to be the rainy season.

With all that eager talent available, there were only a few residual and more domestic occasions in the year when my father was called upon to add his weight, and get dolled up in his slightly-less-than-splendid white Dress Uniform with the row of medals and his white hat with the feathers on top. Nowhere near so imposing as some of the greater dignitaries like the Governor of the Colony, or even the Chief of Police; but it was enough at the time for me to feel the reflected warmth of a minor glory, whenever he put it all on. This helped a good deal when you were nine and so many other people seemed to be ten or eleven...

One of those occasions was Armistice Day. In our present hard-bitten world, that is a commemoration largely gone out of fashion. True, we still go through the motions in an automatic sort of way, but from the time we dropped the actual day November the Eleventh, and shifted our remembrance to 'the nearest Sunday' because it was more convenient, it was evident that we were trying to disguise the awful fact that we have lost interest.

Back in 1936 though, you were only 18 years away from the day of the Armistice itself: everyone's parents had been personally involved. You could, as it were, still smell the mud. What was more, in a community like Kenya the ceremony took on an extra significance which I now suppose was rather ahead of its time. As we stood in my father's office at eleven that morning, looking down upon the War Memorial where he was waiting to lay his official wreath with the others, I can clearly remember how I was struck by the significance of the extraordinary mixture of people taking part. It was not the row of shining decorated big-wigs, the local representatives of a dozen or so countries of Europe, perhaps America, and the various Dominions around the Empire... Nor, even, was it the magnificence of the Band of the K.A.R. – the King's African Rifles – who were poised nearby in a glory of silver and brass and leopard-skins, with the rest of their parade stretching away down the Avenue in a double line of spruce khaki drill, every one topped off by a red fez: that was stirring, but not *moving*. No, the thing that got through to me on that day, and does still, was the strange 'togetherness' of the common crowd. Behind that line of askaris, standing in absolute silence as the distant gun fired, were black men, white men, yellow and brown men... in their best suits, or grubby shorts, brilliant expensive saris, loin-cloths, Sunday garden-party hats, or second-hand pyjamas exposing bare feet... The whole confection spread out across the centre of Nairobi like liquorice-allsorts over a table-top.

The bandsmen suddenly rustled as though a breeze had blown through them, and a moment later "O God our help in ages past" rose up past our window in a massive bewilderment of different accents. I was following the words on my programme, along with the English and the Germans down there, the Africans, the Boers, Indians, Arabs... "Time, like an ever-rolling stream..." All her sons: and there they all were, who – not so many years ago – had been at each other's throats. I sang away like mad.

This was the first time I had actually taken part in the preparations. My mother had taken me along to the British Legion a few days earlier, to help her – with many others – make the wreaths and button-hole poppies from supplies which had been shipped out from England: they were artificial flowers of course, but we had real shiny leaves to add to them. I had produced some pretty dreadful specimens, clumsy-fingered as ever, and no doubt one of the kind ladies dismantled my wreaths after I had gone home and re-made them according to the textbook. However, with my individual poppies I was quite competent, and we had taken a small box of them away with us because it had become a tradition in Nairobi in recent years, to go to the old Military Cemetery outside the town on the edge of the Plains, and place a poppy on every grave.

So in the afternoon when we had changed out of our best clothes, we drove off, making an excursion of it since all the schools closed for the day; and alongside the poppies, with me on the back seat, was the far more interesting hamper containing our picnic.

Almost anywhere on the dusty Plains in those days, you could stop the car with the whole landscape to yourselves, and the grazing herds would amble past...

We drew up by a single scrawny thorn-tree, flat-topped and tattered by generations of giraffe, which leaned out at the roadside with nothing but scrub for miles around. This was 'Lone Tree', a famous local land-mark which for many years epitomised the Kenya countryside in guide-books and souvenir water-colours... As a tree, it wasn't much to write home about; but as a symbol of Life on the Plains, and as a notable meeting-place at night both for lions and for lovers, it was in the history books.

We demolished our picnic, and played some cricket, and then in the late afternoon we continued to the remote cemetery with its rows of crosses and headstones, each with a name, rank and regiment in meticulous letters...

Many families used to join in this simple little pilgrimage, and most of the graves already had a poppy at their head: we were probably the last to arrive.

My parents walked along between the rows, and I followed reading some of the names – in case there were any from families I knew at school, I suppose; though indeed most of the dead, sent from Home to be killed in the German East Africa campaign of 1915, had had no plans whatever to settle here, let alone die in its defence.

We had disposed of all our poppies now, and were heading back to the car with the empty box, in something of a hurry because my parents had to attend a function that night. As I ran after them, something caught my eye. I stopped in my tracks.

Right in the corner of the Cemetery, past the end of the final row, and with no poppy at all, was a pathetic little cross of black wood. It was so hidden by weeds, you could scarcely see it, leaning askew, untended, with the name illegible on its cross-piece. I went up close and peered at it, but no, it was impossible to read.

I called to my father urgently, but he was looking at his watch and beckoning me to the open door of the car.

Quickly I looked around but there was no spare poppy on any nearby grave, and to deprive one of the others would be unfair...

The whole way home I thought silently about this, and the sad loneliness of the unnamed and unremembered grave got worse and worse. On its own, for the rest of the year, that was bad enough: but to have no poppy...! All the emotion of the day was building up inside me, though I sensed that it would be stupid to let it out in public: the grown-ups, after all, had their own lost relatives to remember. To this unknown soldier the respects had to be my own.

While my parents were getting ready for their evening appointment at Government House, I went to see my best friend Jan, who lived down the road.

To him I poured out my feelings, and as usual, he understood at once: of course the little wooden cross should have a poppy, the finest we could produce. He got as worked up as I was, and we would both have been weeping about it by then if we hadn't been so excited making plans...

Jan came back with me for an early supper; and then the grown-ups went off in the car, and under the benevolent and guileless eye of the house-boy Kitau, we were on our own. Jan kept him talking in the kitchen while I slipped out into the hall and dialled the number of Ranji our usual Indian taxi-man, who knew my voice well enough from the frequent times he had run me to or from the school, with which he had a mysterious special relationship... There was always a motor-car crisis at our house: radiators boiled and batteries went flat as often as not, when my mother got into a driving seat.

I even remember the car number: T 1665. "Plague year," my father observed grimly, when he first saw it.

Ranji assumed I was ringing on behalf of my parents and promised to be right along. We told Kitau we would both be at Jan's house till my bedtime, and I would see him then. I took a huge floppy basket called a *kikapu*, which my mother used to have filled with fresh vegetables at the covered market for a shilling a time; and we marched out of the house, purposefully in the direction of Jan's, then doubled back on our tracks to the front gate, there to await Ranji in his peeling silver Chevrolet. Kitau, suspecting nothing, was busy at the cooker making his supper, a mash-up of mealies they called *posho*, and very good too.

"Where's the bwana?" asked Ranji, and we told him that we were the bwanas tonight, so down town please and step on it.

He looked around for my mother. "Come on Ranji," we said, "I bet this useless old tincan won't even *reach* the centre of town. Or have your headlights fallen off?" We also threatened that there had been many criticisms of his vehicle recently, and my father's friend the Chief of Police had asked me my opinion, whether a much more up-to-date taxi firm ought not to have the school contract...

We were down town surprisingly soon. We instructed the muttering Ranji to keep his engine running and his lights off, and out into the gloom we crept with our big kikapu...

A lot of scrambling in the darkness, and a couple of minutes later, we were back. Ranji's eyes opened wider than they had been for thirty years.

"Does your father know," he gasped, "what it is that you are going to be doing?"

"This is official business, Ranji – just drive on."

"Drive on, drive on... Yes yes, I will drive on – straight home I will drive on."

Jan said to me casually: "The Blantyre Garage have brand-new Packards, have you seen?"

I nodded. "And they don't charge waiting time."

Ranji hit himself twice on the forehead, then sighed deeply and switched off the engine. He turned round to us in the back. "You boys now – you are going to be getting me arrested – what is it, what is it that you have got inside that kikapu?"

So in the end we told him. And he, an old soldier himself with a display of grubby medal-ribbons and old Army photos stuck in his driving-mirror, took us straight out to the Military Cemetery without a word of further argument, came in with us while we took the Governor's enormous wreath which we had stolen from the Cenotaph, stood to attention as we laid it on the sad little grave, and sped us home again in silence.

When we got out of the taxi he looked at us man to man, as one of a team that has done a good job. He quite refused to make any charge because, as he said, "It was an event of importance".

I walked in past Kitau who was still stirring his posho. The wireless was broadcasting a repeat of the Armistice Day ceremony. "Time like an ever-rolling stream bears all her sons away," everybody was singing... "They fly forgotten, as a dream dies at the opening day..."

Not forgotten, I said to myself proudly, as I went upstairs to bed.

* * *

'No further comment'

TIM TOPPS

Also by Tim Topps
The Paper Caper (Matador 2013)
Too Long in the Business (Matador 2014)
The Bunny Run (Matador 2015)